TOWLINE

The Story of American Tugboats

TOWLINE

The Story of American Tugboats

by Robert Carse

Illustrated with photographs

W · W · NORTON & COMPANY · INC · NEW YORK

TOWLINE

The Story of American Tugboats

1

NEW YORK is the busiest port in the world. Every twenty minutes a ship comes into her harbor or goes to sea. A good deal more traffic stays inside the harbor and moves day and night. New York's tugboats help the ships, the railroad car floats, the lighters, barges, and scows around the narrow waters. They do a large amount of very necessary work.

So New York has 550 tugboats, more than twice as many as any other port. Within the harbor, the tugs put the seagoing ships alongside their piers, and when the vessels have loaded or unloaded, get them safely started for the open Atlantic. They tow long strings of barges or lighters from one job to another. Ducking around the fast-moving ferry boats that use the same waters, they haul big steel floats loaded with railroad freight cars from New Jersey to Manhattan and back again.

All of this movement might easily cause trouble and serious accidents. The harbor has 650 miles of waterfront and two hundred piers that can take ocean-going ships. Tides and currents are strong; and while there are New York City harbor police, who patrol in launches, and the United States Coast Guard has small, fast craft called picketboats on duty, traffic regulations just as strict as any ashore are kept by the tugboatmen themselves.

The regulations are called the Rules of the Road, and are

established by the Coast Guard. All harbor traffic must obey them. A boat keeps to the right-hand side of a channel, which the sailors, of course, call starboard. One blast made on a boat's whistle means, "I am directing my course to starboard." Two blasts means, "I am directing my course to port." Three blasts tell, "My engines are going at full speed astern." A long blast on the whistle, which lasts for at least seven seconds, means that a tug, or any harbor craft, is coming out from the dock space between two piers into the traffic in the main channel. During fog or snow or heavy rain, a tug that is hauling a tow sounds three blasts: a long one, and then, right after it, two short blasts.

The same regulations are obeyed in all of the other ports along the Atlantic and Pacific coasts; in the Gulf of Mexico; and inland, on the Great Lakes and the rivers. New York, though, because of her size and the amount of her harbor traffic, has an almost unique system for handling her tugboats.

The main tugboat companies have offices on the Manhattan waterfront, alongside famous Battery Park. They are located high in a building with a view out over the Upper Bay and with the Statue of Liberty plainly in sight. The dispatchers who control the movements of the boats owned by their companies can see, through broad windows, a large part of the traffic as it goes back and forth where the two great rivers, the Hudson River and the East River, meet.

A dispatcher is a very important man in the New York tugboat trade. And the chief dispatcher is treated with respect by everybody who works under him. To hold that job, a man has worked hard and long aboard the harbor boats, served also in the seagoing tugs to rescue or salvage ships in distress in the open ocean. He has piloted the greatest of the passenger liners, the *Queens*, the *United States*, and the *Liberté*, moved them in and out of their harbor berths.

All of the dispatchers have been captains of various tugs before being called ashore by the companies. Many of them served in the Navy or the Merchant Marine in World War II, and took part in the Normandy invasion and the island attacks in the Pacific. They have a wide knowledge of the sea.

The biggest of the New York tugboat companies has nine dispatchers on duty. They work in shifts around the clock. Their office is the center of the company's operations, what an army would call its field headquarters. They are constantly in touch with the boats. Orders from them send the tugs on all the various, sometimes strange and sometimes dangerous, tasks around the harbor.

The dispatchers have on their desks a list of each tug's assignments for the day. Shortwave radio sets are used to talk with the tugboat captains and mates, and to exchange messages. On the walls of the big room, there are detailed charts of New York harbor and other coastal and inland ports. The chief dispatcher, who often has a powerful pair of binoculars in his hands, stands at the window that overlooks the Narrows, past Liberty Island and the Verrazano Bridge. Other men squint through telescopes to identify an incoming ship or a tug on her way back from a job in the Lower Bay.

Radio telephones ring almost constantly in the dispatchers' office. The conversations are short. A tugboat mate reports that some barges have just been hauled to their destination and delivered. "What's next?" He is told what and where, says, "O.K.," and hangs up his phone in the pilothouse of the tug.

The ticker-tape machine clacks busily in the rear of the office. A dispatcher goes to it every few minutes and reads off the information it carries. That can tell of the arrival of a foreign passenger liner at the government quarantine station on Staten Island, or a tanker that has passed City Island on her way down the East River. Tugboat movements and the wind

The dispatchers' office at Moran Towing and Transportation Company where four eagle-eyed, cool-nerved men handle the operations of the largest tugboat fleet in the Port of New York. They work with a practically unobstructed view of the harbor, twenty-five stories above Battery Place at the southerly tip of Manhattan Island. Two of the dispatchers shown are talking with company tugboat captains by radio telephone.

and sea conditions are also reported over the ticker.

The dispatchers need it all for the decisions they must make before they give orders to the boats. Their favorite piece of equipment is the radio telephone, and the officers aboard the boats share their liking for it. The old-timers can recall when all they had was "the squawk box"—the shortwave radio. Signals were often blurred with static and unintelligible. One famous chief dispatcher, Captain Daniel Anglim, used to go out onto a small balcony from a window on the twenty-fifth floor of the building. All he needed was his lung power and a megaphone.

He had served as mate in sailing ships as a young man and never had trouble making himself heard. The Moran Company, for which Captain Anglim worked, docked its boats at Pier One and Pier Two, almost directly below the building. But at the height where he stood there was always wind, and down below were all the city sounds and the harbor noises.

Captain Anglim was not often asked to repeat himself. The orders he called through the big megaphone struck straight past all the interference. Gulls and pigeons screeched in fright and flew away from their nearby perches. Taxi drivers stared up, their eyes wide with amazement; there was a man who could shout louder than a traffic cop.

The captains and mates aboard the Moran tugs in the 1920's and 1930's had seen Captain Anglim come out onto the balcony. They were ready for the long-carrying bellow, and to them it was very plain. They answered Captain Anglim with a whistle toot or a hand wave. Then the bowline was cast off by the deckhand, and the boat that was ordered to a new job backed from the pier and gathered full speed in the river.

While Captain Anglim's lung power is remembered with admiration, tugboatmen say the radio telephone is much better. They are pleased, too, by the way they can read the messages flashed at night on the upright steel panel outside a window of the dispatchers' office. Those help them plenty as they come up the bay after dark to find out about the next job.

Tugboat crews and dispatchers are able to work together with complete understanding because they are friends, and often old shipmates. People who have never been around tugboatmen before are surprised by the way they talk to each other. Everybody aboard a boat is called by his first name— except the captain. He is called "Cap," and sometimes the mate or the chief engineer uses his first name or a nickname he got when he was a deckhand.

For generations, a number of families in the Bay Ridge section of Brooklyn and on Staten Island have sent their sons to work aboard the harbor boats. Boys who in their early teens lay awake at night during a "pea-soup" fog and listened to the tug signals out in the bay, and checked each one, made a logical decision. They shipped out as deckhands aboard the tugs. This is the beginning, the apprentice job for a boy who hopes to serve as captain. He waits his chance and joins the tugboatmen's union, then waits again until he can find work with the company with which he wants to stay.

Most harbor tugs carry a crew of nine men whose ages may range from seventeen to sixty-five. They are made up of a captain, a mate, an engineer, a fireman or oiler who works in the engine room, a couple of deckhands, and a cook. The bigger tugs that run offshore and do ocean work have as many as twenty men. The additional crew members aboard them include a radio operator, a second mate, an assistant engineer, another oiler or fireman, more deckhands, and a messboy to clean up the galley and help the cook.

Nobody who works aboard a tugboat wears a uniform. The captain, though, does wear shore-going, street clothes and sometimes a tie. The mate and the engineer wear khakis, and in cold weather the mate puts on a loud checked mackinaw coat or a windbreaker. The rest of the crew, except the cook, wear blue denim shirts and dungarees. The cook, because of his galley duties, has on a spotless, short-sleeved white shirt and an equally clean apron.

Food aboard a tugboat is plentiful and good. Three big meals a day are served, starting with six A.M. breakfast. Coffee is always ready in a tall urn, and milk and fruit juices are handy in the galley refrigerator. For men who are working at night, or are just plain hungry, the cook keeps in the refrigerator what is known as "night lunch." It generally consists of slices of meat and cheese, pie, cake, fresh fruit. Doughnuts, bread, and crackers are kept on the galley table with all kinds of jam, honey, and condiments.

Tugboat quarters are small, but comfortable. A man has a steel-pipe bunk with a good mattress, and locker space for his gear. It is all he needs aboard a harbor craft; the ocean-going tugs have larger quarters called fo'c'sles. An ocean-going crew is sometimes offshore for as long as a month or more.

A tugboat crew works hard, and the usual day is eight hours long. A man who does additional work is paid overtime, at so much an hour, with the rates set by the union. Average pay for a crew member is 600 dollars a month. A captain makes around 30 dollars a day, and a deckhand about 16 dollars, including his overtime pay.

For this, a deckhand works hard enough. Many crews stay aboard their boats for sixty or seventy hours straight. A regular routine of daily jobs is checked by the mate. Between docking and undocking operations, when the big hawsers known as "towlines" must be tended, the tug is kept in shape.

Decks and ventilators and the pilothouse and the deckhouse and the railings must be scraped down to the steel, then painted. Cabins are swabbed out; a powerful solution called

Tugboats are famous for the abundance and quality of their food. Here the captain, on the left, and Bill Quick seem quite satisfied. The captain, on his way back to the pilothouse, happily accepts some coconut cake from the cook.

soogey and made of lye and coarse soap is used to keep bulk-heads clean. The big brass bitts around which the towing hawsers are secured are polished until they gleam. Log fenders, which protect the tug while it is alongside another vessel or a pier, are always in need of repair. Pieces of manila line taken from old hawsers are wound in neat, close turns around the long logs, and the rope bridles at the tops are renewed if they have chafed thin against the cleats that hold them in place.

Hawsers that have been used in a docking operation or for a tow must be hauled aft and stowed neatly on the gratings on the wide deck at the stern of the boat. Sometimes a hawser has been injured because of the great pressure put on it. The injured section weakens the entire hawser, which is usually about 200 feet long and 6 inches in diameter. With the mate to show him, a new deckhand learns how to splice.

The injured part of the hawser is removed, cut out strand by strand. Then the ends of the individual strands are tied so they will keep their shape as the splice is made. Strand is tucked back against strand, the two ends of the rope brought together like entwined fingers. A big hardwood tool that is nearly the size of a baseball bat, called a fid, is used to open the stiff strands in the sections of the rope being spliced. Then the strands are beaten tight and smooth, so they fully interlock, by the broad end of the fid and a heavy wooden mallet.

A new deckhand begins to think he is on his way to being a real sailor once he has made a hawser splice. His next accomplishment is to make a monkey's fist. This is usually done with small, quarter-inch-diameter manila line. It is called a monkey's fist because the line is led three times one way, then three times another, and then three through the other parts. The result, when tightened up, looks vaguely like something

HANS MARX

While the tug waits for orders, one of her crew makes use of summer sunlight and the hawsers he has neatly stowed on the afterdeck.

that might belong to a monkey, but is considerably bigger than any fist he would own.

A tugboatman's monkey's fist is secured to the end of a light manila line that serves a very important purpose. This, with the monkey's fist attached, is known as a heaving line. It is used constantly in harbor work to get hawsers aboard ships or onto a dock. The hawsers in themselves are too heavy to be moved more than a short distance. A deckhand who can flip the loop at the end of a hawser onto a dock bollard unaided is called "cowboy" by his shipmates and is considered really skillful.

Handling a heaving line also takes a fair amount of skill. The line is kept supple by being stretched often, then carefully and evenly coiled. When a deckhand is ready to make a cast, he divides the heaving-line coil in two parts, keeping most in his left hand. He throws with his right, which holds the monkey's fist end. When the tug is close enough for him to make his cast—and some veteran deckhands can send a heaving line almost 100 feet—he brings back his right arm in a long, smooth swing. Then he sweeps his hand up, out, and lets go. He has already estimated the wind effect, the speed of the tug and of the other vessel, and the distance needed for the cast.

The line spirals in the air behind the monkey's fist, and the line runs out rapidly as the deckhand loosens his left hand. Aboard the other vessel, a man is waiting to make the catch. He grabs fast at the line before the wind or the motion of the vessels can drag it over the side. Then he shouts or waves to the tugboat deckhand.

The end of the heaving line the deckhand holds is secured to the hawser, and the hawser is coiled, ready to be hauled aboard the other vessel. Men aboard her drag in the hawser hand over hand, and it is brought on deck and secured. Slack is taken up as the tugboat begins to tow, and millions of dol-

With the lower Manhattan skyline in the background, a tugboat crew member stands at the bow, docking hawser ready. He and his kind are proud that they can secure a tug with a single cast of a hawser, throwing the rope immediately onto an upright dock log, or a cleat. So their name for themselves is "cowboys." Forward of this man is a bow fender made of old hawsers.

lars worth of vessel and cargo are safely moved by the single connecting hawser.

A deckhand, as he works around New York harbor, learns many things that add to the knowledge which will make him a pilot. He gets to know thoroughly the buoyage system that marks the ship channels of the upper and lower bays. Night jobs instruct him about the lights of other vessels, and the characteristic signals of lighthouses and lighted buoys. The captain and the mate are patient with him; they explain the great need for what they call "night eyes." They recommend that off-watch, on his time below, the deckhand should study the Rules of the Road. He can never get his license and sail the harbor as an officer unless he has memorized them.

The most important rule is:

> *A steam vessel when towing another vessel or vessels alongside or by pushing ahead shall, in addition to her sidelights, carry two bright white lights in a vertical line, one over the other, not less than three feet apart, and when towing one or more vessels astern, regardless of the length of the tow, shall carry an additional bright white light three feet above or below such lights. Each of these lights shall be of the same construction and character, and shall be carried in the same position as the white light mentioned in article 2 (a) or the after range light mentioned in article 2 (f).*

The young deckhand reads that and reads it again. The technical language is a bit hard for him to understand. But then he is sure of the meaning. Range lights are the two white lights a vessel carries, the one forward lower than the one aft.

The third shows that she is towing, and should be given plenty of clearance astern. They are visible for a distance of five miles. His own boat, right here, carries them.

The rule still seems to be written in lawyer language. The deckhand gets up from his chair at the galley table. He has been sitting alone, studying during his off-watch in the night. He goes over to the galley door and looks out across the river in the darkness.

But the darkness is not complete. Shore lights reach out over the water all around the bay. They dim the lights that the vessels show. The rule to make the vessels' lights seen at a distance of five miles is necessary. That distance is measured, too, for clear-weather conditions. During most nights, though, there is haze over the water, or fog.

The deckhand remembers a day not long ago when scrub growth out on the New Jersey flats caught fire, and all through the night thick smoke drifted over the Hudson. There were other times when great, gray banks of smog, a foul mixture of fog and smoke, came out from Brooklyn and Long Island City or the Bronx upon the East River.

Range lights gave the man at the wheel up in the pilothouse of a tugboat the exact location of another boat. He could tell by the angle of those lights, and by her red and green sidelights, which way she was headed and her approximate speed.

The old seamen's rule, good for all men aboard any kind of craft, was to be remembered. It said, "Green to green"—that meant starboard side to starboard side—"and red to red, all is safe, so go ahead."

It makes very good sense, the deckhand tells himself, and once more repeats it. He stands for a long time in the galley doorway, looking out at the changing patterns of the harbor lights.

Over there, a buoy winks, and then another, and another. The tug, riding without a tow, pounds along the channel at top speed, the captain eager to finish the next job and get home to his family. The deckhand looks out on tugs that move much more slowly, hauling tows. He can identify them by the lights they show, their silhouettes, and the company emblems they wear on their stacks.

But the deckhand, thinking of the examination he must pass before he takes a pilot's job, is interested in the various combinations of lights aboard the tugs and their tows. Those have a special meaning, and are required by the Coast Guard.

Here, in inland waters, a tug that is towing one or more vessels shows the necessary three white lights in a vertical line on her foremast, and in addition her red and green sidelights. The vessels being towed carry sidelights, but no mast lights. When a tug is pushing a tow instead of hauling it, she shows two amber lights from her stern.

Dredges working at deepening the harbor put up at night a pair of red lights that tell what they are doing and where they are. A vessel that is moored over submarine construction carries three red lights in a vertical line. When a tug hauls scows abreast in the Hudson River, each scow has a white light on her outboard corners, fore and aft.

The deckhand tells himself that he has plenty to learn in the three years before he can take his Coast Guard examination. But there is one thing he knows very clearly right now, and will never forget. The traffic cops for the Port of New York or for any port are the men on duty in the pilothouses. Their knowledge, their keen eyesight, and the ability to make the right decision in an emergency are what keep the harbor craft safe.

MORRIS ROSENFELD

Dalzelleagle *heads up-harbor at full speed past the Statue of Liberty. That is a handsome gilt eagle on her pilothouse topside just abaft the searchlight. The tall ladders beside the stack are for boarding purposes. When a ship is being docked, the tug captain boards her to advise the shipmaster.*

2

FOR HER SIZE, a modern tugboat is more powerful than any other craft used in regular trade. Only some very special types of Navy vessels have greater horsepower. The tugs that work in the Port of New York or any of the other coastal harbors are about 100 feet long. Great Lakes tugs are smaller and have less engine power. The "towboats" used on the Ohio River and on the Mississippi are built differently and will be discussed later in another chapter.

A new tugboat delivered in 1969 for service in coastal waters cost her owners several million dollars. The Moran Company owns four fine craft that were recently added to her fleet. They are sister vessels, the *Teresa, Joan, Doris,* and *Elizabeth.* Their length is 110 feet, and their diesel engines give them 4,290 horsepower apiece.

They have short, streamlined stacks and long afterdecks. When they are free from a tow and moving across the harbor at full speed, driven by their twin propellers, they are a pretty sight. A big, feathery wake rises up astern, and towards it rushes the white splatter of water from the bow wash.

Until just a few years ago, tugboats protected their bows with what their crews called "beards"—thick mats made from the ends of old hawsers and all kinds of rope. Those kept a boat from hurting herself while she strained hard to push some huge liner into a slip, or lay bow-to at a dock where the river current ran fast. But then nylon line replaced manila. It is a good deal more expensive and lasts much longer. So the tugboat owners ordering a new boat specified that rubber mats cover the bow.

Those are made of very strong rubber, the kind used in automobile tires, but considerably thicker. They are not as rugged-looking as the old beards, but they do the job much better. The new Moran boats are equipped with them, and as a result have a very neat, slim look.

The four sister boats have been given all of the latest equipment. Up in the pilothouse are double steering controls, with another set aft on the top of the deckhouse. The boats can be handled from either point, according to the needs of the captain and the mate. The pilothouse is also equipped with radar, a gyroscope compass, which operates with practically no error, loran for offshore navigation use, a radio direction finder, a standard radio, a VHF radio, a batteryless telephone, and a searchlight.

The pair of diesel engines down in the compact, bright engine room provide 1,950 shaft horsepower each at 900 revolutions a minute. That means a combined drive of 4,290 horsepower. Twin 10-foot 9-inch, 3-blade propellers, matched right and left, move the boat. Twin rudders are used, which give a swing of 90 degrees and plenty of maneuvering ability.

The boats' hulls were completely tank-tested at the Wagnenigen Towing Tank in Holland before work on them was finished and they were delivered to the Moran Company. Each of these tugs has accommodations for eleven crewmen, with fully air-conditioned quarters and galley. There is only one difference between the sister craft. *Joan* and *Elizabeth* have been equipped with automatic towing winches for offshore work.

A winch of the kind used aboard them is electrically powered and has a huge barrel. The barrel is horizontal with the deck and built of sturdy steel. Wound around it is 2,100 feet of towing cable. This is 2¼ inches in diameter and can take thousands of tons of strain before it breaks. It is made of the finest quality plowshare steel.

The cable has been led very carefully around the winch barrel, each turn exactly in place so it will not foul or jam. When the tug is under way and has a tow astern of her, in either good or bad weather, there is usually great strain on the cable. The winch responds to this. It lets out a few more feet of slack as the towed craft bucks a wave or yaws off course, and tightens up the cable when the craft being towed surges unexpectedly ahead. A man standing there in control of the winch could never handle it as efficiently as the automatic electric device.

During some of their time ashore, men in the tugboat crews who have a real interest in their work borrow books of maritime history from the public libraries. They read them at home or when they are off watch back aboard the boats. They find that the stories of the early days of the trade are fascinating.

No tug, in the first 150 years of the trade, had anything like an automatic winch device. All work was done by clumsy steam winches or by hand. In winter, the steam pipes leading along the exposed decks often froze solid. Then, after they had been thawed out, there was danger from the thick coating of ice on the hawsers or the cables, on the winch barrels, and the decks of the tugs. Axes were used to knock away the ice, and sand was sprinkled across the decks. Still, accidents happened. Men slipped and broke their legs. They caught their fingers between the icy turns of a hawser and a winch barrel and lost their fingertips. Towboating, as it was called in the early days, could be very rough work.

The first tugboat, the history books say, was the *Charlotte Dundas*, built in 1801 in Scotland. She was moved by a single paddle wheel shaped like a barrel. It was fitted in a wellhole in her stern. This was almost exactly like the space indented in the stern of a modern boat to take an outboard motor.

Charlotte Dundas hauled barges on the Forth and Clyde Canal across Scotland. Her design was followed by other stern-wheeler boats of the kind later used in many parts of the world, and particularly on the Mississippi River. The side-wheeler boats had more power, but needed more room in which to maneuver.

Old-time sailors, men who worked aboard the square-riggers, had their own name for a tugboat. They called her "a fair wind ahead." The famous clipper ships, *Rainbow, Comet, Flying Cloud, Cutty Sark,* and all the rest were towed in and out of harbor by tugs. It was possible with certain tide and wind conditions for a clipper captain to sail alongside his dock in the Port of New York. But in the Port of London, for instance, where many American ships were often sent, it was impossible. Tugs were also greatly needed in ports like Boston, Philadelphia, Baltimore, Charleston, Savannah, and New Orleans. Most of them were situated on rivers too narrow and too fast to be navigated by a square-rigged vessel.

Tugboats found plenty of business, too, on the Great Lakes. They were used to tow schooners up the sharp bends of the Detroit River and the St. Marys River. When the wind was wrong, they were hailed by eager customers right out in the middle of the lakes, and hauled strings of schooners, or barges, or large rafts of timber to the various ports.

Pittsburgh, on the Ohio, became a big tugboat-building port. Henry Fulton and his partners started construction work there in 1815 after being successful on the Hudson. Fulton used the construction ideas developed as early as 1787 by John Fitch, who for a short time ran a steamboat on the Delaware River. Fitch's boat lacked power, though, and could not buck the river current and keep a regular schedule. The same was true for Fulton and his partners until they finally realized they should enlarge the boilers and the engines in their boats, and put the machinery up on the main decks and not down in the lower sections of the hulls.

The first tugboat in business in the Port of New York was the 146-foot steamer *Nautilus*. She began hauling for hire on January 26, 1818, when she went to Sandy Hook at the entrance of the harbor. The sailing ship *Corsair*, inward bound from Charleston, was waiting for her. *Nautilus*, a side-wheeler with a 30-horsepower steam engine, towed the other vessel up the bay to quarantine and the next day to Old Slip Wharf in Manhattan.

When the Erie Canal, connecting the Great Lakes with the Hudson River, was opened in 1825, there was a great need for tugboats. They towed the hundreds of barges and scows from the canal entrance to New York, and made the trip back up-river with other "strings" of loaded craft.

The men who owned sloops and ketches and schooners and still believed sail was better than steam, were soon out of business. Some of them would not leave the river without a fight. They rammed their vessels bow-on and under full sail into tugboats. There were serious collisions, boats were sunk, and crews flung in the water.

Before 1860 and the Civil War, tall-stacked tugs that burned coal and had thick wooden hulls were a familiar sight in any American seaport. New York kept the biggest fleet because of the amount of her harbor traffic. Several former passenger boats were turned into tugs. They were fast, could get around at ten or twelve miles an hour when not under tow, and could make almost half that speed, wind and tide favorable, with a vessel hauled astern.

It took almost one hundred years before all of the coal-burners and wooden-hulled tugboats were laid up, permanently out of commission. Steel hulls had come into use, and diesel engines instead of those driven by steam power. Tugs had taken a very active part in World War II, and had proven themselves in action. They towed ammunition and supplies across the Atlantic and served at the beachheads in the Normandy invasion.

With the end of the war in 1945, the main American tugboat companies were ready to build high-speed boats equipped with diesel power. Moran and McAllister and Dalzell, the three largest operators in the Port of New York, ordered vessels of modern design, and put them in service. Moran took special pride in the boat that was christened *Alice L. Moran* at her launching.

She is the world's most powerful ocean-going tug. Her diesels turn up 9,600 horsepower. She can haul practically anything that floats anywhere there is enough water for her and her tow.

A great deal of history has been made here in the Port of New York since *Nautilus* went to Gravesend Bay in 1818 and put a hawser aboard the Charleston-owned sailing ship.

3

ONE OF THE most important parts of a tugboatman's education is learning every detail about his home port. A smart young deckhand in Boston, for instance, can give the names and the exact locations of the islands that make navigation quite tricky there. He is able to discern at night, by their sound signals and the light characteristics, the buoys that mark Main Ship Channel. He is fully familiar with Outer Brewster, Middle Brewster, Lighthouse Island, and the Calf Islands, Georges and Gallops; and Castle and Governors Islands.

A deckhand working in the Port of Philadelphia has learned about the Delaware River from Cape May, at the entrance, to the lower river ports at Lewes and Marcus Hook and Chester. All of the city docks at Philadelphia are familiar to him, and the lights that mark the Walt Whitman Bridge and are a great aid in fog. He knows ice conditions in the winter months and their effects on a tow, and the positions of the abandoned lighthouses whose tall brick towers are the homes of thousands of gulls along the ship channel.

Baltimore crews know the broad reaches of the Chesapeake from end to end. When they have a chance, they swap information with the men who work aboard the boats stationed at Norfolk and Hampton Roads and Newport News, near the mouth of the bay. They sail the many small rivers that run into the bay, and haul gasoline barges into backwater creeks where the barge bottoms slide through mud and occasionally bump over a sunken tree trunk.

New Orleans has no finger piers—so named because of the way they stick out from the shore. The Mississippi is too powerful for the kind of construction used in New York. All of the ships that use the Louisiana port tie up alongside the levee, bows pointed into the current. When a tow leaves her berth, a tug crew must work fast, or Old Big Muddy will yank her out of control. New Orleans tugboatmen are held in high respect in any port in the Gulf of Mexico.

Fog is the great problem on the West Coast. Men handling the tugs in the harbors from San Pedro to Seattle have developed the same kind of skill. They use sound to determine where they are during a spell of gray-green fog that sometimes lasts for days and keeps them from seeing the bow of the boat from the pilothouse window. Whistle blasts, even bounced back from an object as small as a channel buoy, tell a trained man

HANS MARX

Three Dalzell tugs swing the deeply loaded Atlantic Traveler *into the channel and leave her to her pilot.*

The very early morning sun shining on her stack, a freight ship, riding high, comes up New York Bay past the Verrazano Bridge.

quite accurately how far away the buoy is, and its location in relation to the boat that sent the blast. The sound bounced back from another vessel is different, and so is that from a larger surface, a warehouse alongside a dock, a seawall, or land itself.

There is plenty of nervous strain in this kind of piloting, because it is partly guesswork. West Coast tugboatmen solemnly promise to give up their jobs, go live and work in sun-filled ports like Honolulu. But they stay in the foggy ports, and leave only when younger men are ready to take their places and they finally retire.

San Francisco and New York are the only two American seaports where the big ocean-going liners frequently dock. But, even with her very large Pacific trade, San Francisco does not attract the wide variety of shipping that moves past Sandy

Hook. New York is used by vessels of every kind that come to it from all around the world.

One of the hardest jobs for a New York tugboat crew is handling a tanker loaded with gasoline. Most of them are docked in back of Staten Island, where the bottom of the channel is solid granite, and the steel bottoms of the tankers are just a few inches above it at high tide. The tugs move the tankers with the greatest care, and always when the water is high. It is a much easier job to take a 20,000-ton Greek tanker from Stapleton, in the Narrows off Staten Island, to her unloading berth at a dock at 138th Street in the Bronx.

The tug's captain first goes aboard the tanker to serve as her harbor pilot. He has already checked her draft, found out how much water she needs for safe handling. She is deeply loaded, and draws 34 feet forward and 34 feet aft. This is a job where the ship must be docked at high tide, and the tug captain wants to be absolutely sure that she will have enough water under her at her Bronx dock. He has checked the depth there at high tide on the chart in his pilothouse.

The deckhand on watch aboard the tugboat tosses a heaving line when the captain is ready to leave. It is caught by a sailor on the foredeck of the tanker and a hawser is hauled over and secured. Then the deckhand moves a tall wooden ladder in place on the deckhouse of the tug, the upper end braced firmly against the main-deck rail of the other vessel.

The tugboat captain nimbly climbs the ladder. He crosses the deck to the long, raised catwalk that runs fore and aft on the tanker. He disappears through a doorway in the tanker's deckhouse, and reappears up on her bridge. The tanker is flying a red and white signal flag on her bridge halyards. It is the "H" flag of the International Code, which means the ship has a pilot aboard.

The tanker has hauled up her anchor. The tug clears her

hawser and backs away into the channel. She will accompany the tanker and help later with another tug in the docking operation. Now both the tug and the tanker start upstream towards Governors Island at the foot of Manhattan, the tanker in the lead.

The tug deckhand has a few spare minutes to look at the harbor. Here, spread before him, are the magnificent harbor and the great buildings of the Wall Street district. He is once more impressed, and feels a sense of pride. All around him, the waterborne traffic moves.

He remembers that more than 4,000 tugs, railroad car floats, lighters, barges, and scows are in daily use in the port. They shuttle between ship and shore and ship and ship. A hundred heavy-lift derricks, which can lift as much as 250 tons are in use. There are 144 dry-storage and twenty cold-storage warehouses, 160 transit sheds, 372 storage tanks, and 3 grain elevators, each of which holds 4¼ million bushels.

The deckhand is pleased to recall these facts. But there is another piece of information, recently learned, that gives him more satisfaction. An open-decked lighter, in common use all over the harbor for cargo work, got its name back in old sailing-ship days. The square-riggers anchored in Gravesend Bay or in behind Staten Island while they "lightered off" several hundred tons of their cargo. Then the early towboats came alongside and hauled them to the Manhattan docks, where the rest of the unloading was done.

The deckhand, his heaving line coiled and ready for the next pitch, the hawser carefully stowed in neat coils on the afterdeck, still has another couple of minutes of freedom. He ducks into the galley to get a mug of coffee, then stands at the bow again, the breeze whipping at his cap visor and the hem of his windbreaker. New York because of the rapid flow of her two main rivers carries a large quantity of flotsam around the harbor; old, water-soaked timber, planks, and creosoted spiles that served as uprights for abandoned docks, are a constant menace to navigation.

The deckhand reports what he sees to the pilothouse. A 15-foot-long spile 12 inches in diameter and heavy with a combination of creosote and sea water can take a propeller blade off the strongest-built tug. The mate, standing at the wheel in the pilothouse, also keeps a sharp watch as he steers. Millions of dollars of damage are done each year in the Port of New York by flotsam.

Now the tug, the Greek tanker about 200 yards ahead of her, has Governors Island abeam on the starboard side. The deckhand glances over at the close huddle of brick barracks and officers' quarters that belong to the United States First Army and the Coast Guard and remembers that Confederate prisoners were kept in the casemates of gray, grim Castle William during the Civil War. Beyond Governors Island, between its northerly tip and the southern end of Manhattan, is the busiest section of the harbor.

Ships are putting out to sea through the narrow stretch of water, or inward bound. Tugs with tows or railroad-car floats alongside steer courses past them. Ferry boats from Staten Island and Governors Island come in for a landing at their Manhattan slips; then, their whistles shrill, they take off for the return trip.

The deckhand is glad that he is not yet ready to take his pilot's examination. Let the mate up there at the wheel in the pilothouse have the responsibility. This is a hot corner, and seems to have more traffic every day. Right here, too, is the bad patch of current called the Spider. It swings around between the Battery and Governors Island with surprising force. Farther along, in the East River, is the stretch called Hell Gate, even on the charts. That is where the rising tide coming in from Sandy Hook and the ocean meets the rising tide coming from the other direction and Long Island Sound. The result is one of the worst tide rips ever met by any sailor.

But the captain of the tug has chosen exactly the right time to bring the tanker into Hell Gate and pilot her through it to her dock upriver. The water now, at full high tide, is quiet, almost unruffled. The deckhand stands relaxed.

He notices how the captain changes course off Corlears Hook on the Manhattan side, and again with some tall stacks in line near Wallabout Bay on the Brooklyn side. The mate follows the same courses, and the deckhand stares up at the vast reach of Brooklyn Bridge overhead, then Manhattan Bridge, then Williamsburg. Other bridges, Queensborough and Triborough, are ahead, but the deckhand looks around at the old Brooklyn Navy Yard. The captain and the mate have told him stories about when the yard had every foot of space filled during World War II, and the big battleships and aircraft carriers would take down their topmasts to sail under the Brooklyn Bridge.

Now the islands, Ward's and Blackwells, are ahead in the river where the channel forks and narrows. The mate calls down and tells the deckhand to go get dinner while there is still time. Another tug from the same company has moved up from astern and will help in the docking operation. The fuel terminal where the tanker will tie up is not too far away.

The deckhand comes back to work happily, full of soup, bread, pork chops, potatoes, salad, and pie, and finds that the tanker has slowed to half speed. The docking operation is about to begin. Heaving line in hand, the deckhand motions to a sailor on the tanker's deck. The other man nods; the two vessels are close and the wind is right.

The toss is made and caught, and the hawser goes over to the tanker's forward bitts. The second tug has made fast aft, on the other side of the vessel. The tanker slowly heads around, the tugs both pushing and hauling, and with her engines and rudder in use, until she is broadside in the river. The tugs hold her there while the various whistle signals from the tanker's bridge direct them. A whistle-blast code is used: Slow Ahead, Full Ahead, Full Astern, and Stop Heaving.

When the tanker is completely squared away, her own engines move her. She heads into the slip, the tugs still aiding her fore and aft, one on each side. Then she has her hawsers down on the dock, and is made fast. Her bow and stern wind-lasses begin to thump as the steam valves are opened, power is applied, and the hawsers tightened. She lies exactly in line with the leads to the shoreside tanks and soon will start pumping out her cargo. A final toot comes from her whistle, given by the tugboat captain who has served as pilot. The job is done.

The young deckhand aboard the tug gets his heaving line back from the tanker. He steadies the ladder as the captain returns to the tug. Then he hauls aboard the hawser.

The captain goes up into the pilothouse to report to the company office by radio telephone. He talks with a dispatcher and receives the orders for the next job. The deckhand takes care to listen to the conversation, standing right below the pilothouse on the foredeck.

The next job is towing a string of hopper barges in Raritan Bay. The deckhand feels sudden pangs of hunger. He hurries into the galley for a handful of doughnuts and a mug of coffee, and to find out what the cook is going to serve for supper.

4

IT TAKES AN AVERAGE of twenty-five years of harbor work before a New York tugboat captain is ready to dock one of the big passenger liners. He has handled all kinds of smaller vessels, but to dock a ship like the *Queen Elizabeth* or the *United States* means that he is at the very top of his trade. Docking a large liner can be both dangerous and very expensive.

Tugs have been lost during a docking operation, crushed between the ship and the pier when a sudden gust of wind came in off the river. Snapped hawsers have broken deckhands' legs. Severe damage has been done to piers when wind and current combined against the pilot.

A ship has very little braking power, a good deal less than an automobile. She cannot help herself when she is in a tight situation, although her engines are working full astern. And a modern tug with more than 4,000 horsepower can very easily bend a ship's side plates as she pushes hard to get the big vessel into her slip. So tugboat captains do their best to bring the bows of their boats against a hull frame. Those solid steel supports can be located along the shipside where two hull plates meet. But sometimes it is impossible to find a spot where a frame is available, or the currents swing the tug's bow away and onto the tender plates.

These are just a few of a docking pilot's problems. Men have

Sailors call the Statue of Liberty the "Old Lady." Here it is in the background as the French Line's fine passenger ship Flandre *arrives and is given a spectacular welcome by a New York City fire boat, all monitor nozzles open.*

fallen between the tug and the pier while handling hawsers in slippery winter weather. A hawser may be pulled under the stern of the liner, and the tug capsized and her entire crew pitched in the water. Collisions between ships are always possible. Tugs that tussle the liners into their dock space in the Hudson River are hampered by bottom mud that reduces power and slows the movements of the liner herself, because she sits deeper in the stuff.

A big liner is almost always docked during what is called slack water, the period of an hour or so between two tides. Slack water, though, is never exactly that in New York harbor. A current of some kind keeps on running. The East River is so uneasy and narrow, with the channel only 500 feet wide in some places, that the owners of the liners refuse to dock their vessels in it.

But the Hudson River, even though it has been dredged and deepened, makes docking work very hard. During the months between November and April, strong northwest winds blow. That means the ebb—falling—tides last longer than usual. The level of the water drops then as much as four feet. Currents swing from side to side of the channel, bouncing off the New Jersey shore against the Manhattan piers and back again.

There are today less than fifty pilots in the Port of New York who are qualified to dock a liner of more than 30,000 tons. They take over the handling of the ships from the harbor pilots, men of equal skill, who have boarded out off the Ambrose Light Station at the entrance to the harbor. The captains of the ships being docked watch every move they make, because, according to the law, a captain has the final responsibility for the safety of a vessel. Sometimes, during strikes, captains have tried to dock liners without tugs or pilots, and in most cases banged up the ships and the piers.

A docking pilot takes over from the harbor pilot in the Hud-

The sleek passenger ship Rotterdam *of the Holland–American Line is worked alongside her New York pier by tugs.*

son River, within short distance of the pier. The chief dispatcher of the tugboat company has sent as many tugs as he thinks are needed for the job. He figures this out from the size of the ship, her draft, and the wind and tide conditions. The Moran Company has published a detailed list of these requirements, and they should be printed here. Other New York pilots, working for the McAllister Brothers Company, use a list pretty much like it or keep one in their heads. A Moran pilot is told to consider:

(1) *The velocity of current on the ebb and flow of tide.*

(2) *The direction and velocity of the wind.*

(3) *The effect of this wind on the surface flow of the tide as well as upon the vessel, particularly one of more than 30,000 tons.*

(4) *The time elapsing between high water at Governors Island and the start of ebb tide at midchannel at 23rd Street, Hudson River.*

(5) *The time elapsing between high water at Governors Island and the start of ebb tide at the pierheads; on the river bottom.*

(6) *The effect of current on ships of more than 30,000 tons.*

The docking pilot handles a liner from the inboard (inside) wing of her bridge. He directs the quartermaster who is at the wheel in the ship's wheelhouse and is still actually steering the ship. But once the tugs are alongside and have their lines secured, a ship uses her propellers and rudder only for very short periods of time. The tugs do nearly all the work.

A code of whistle signals is used between the pilot and the skippers of the tugs taking part in the job. They work for the

The freighter Chickasaw, *of Mobile, is towed out of her slip, her propeller thrashing, the towline taut. The tug captain stands at the auxiliary steering station at the after end of the boat deck, where he can watch every part of the operation.*

same company and know him well. He is the senior skipper among those called by the dispatcher; the mate handles his tug in his absence aboard the liner. When weather is bad in the river, as many as eight tugs team up to get the ship docked. In fair weather, four are enough. The usual number is six.

The docking pilot talks to the tugs in what seems like a rapid jumble of sounds to people on the piers who don't understand the signal code. It is really simple. He uses a mouth whistle for the tugs that work forward of the ship's bridge, and the much deeper-bellowing ship's whistle for those aft. When he signals, the tugs push, pull, stop, or start, at the bow and stern of the liner. One whistle blast means stop or, if the tug isn't moving, to go slowly ahead. Two blasts mean to go astern, and a series of quick blasts means full astern. Each tug skipper answers with his own whistle, repeating the signal, so that the pilot knows that it has been received and is being obeyed.

Tugboat skippers in the pilothouses of the boats turn the big steering wheels with one hand and with the other work the levers that control the engines. The tugs at the bow push downstream. Those at the stern pull her upstream. When more power is needed, two tugs work together in tandem, with a hawser stretched between them.

The liner is brought around in the channel and almost against the pierhead amidships. This is called "the knuckle," and the pilot uses it as a pivot. He swings the ship there, slowly, carefully, talking to the tugs all the time and with an occasional order to the quartermaster at the ship's wheel.

It is, after that, almost like docking the Greek tanker in her East River slip. When the liner is headed straight into her berth, her own engines gently move her. She slides forward, the pilot leaning out over the bridge wing, the captain of the ship right beside him. They study the measurements marked in big yellow numerals on the dock shed roof and on the pier.

Five tugs take their stations before docking Queen Mary. *Assigned to this duty by their company dispatchers, they have been assembled from all over the harbor.*

Handsome all-white Empress of Canada *is brought into her North River slip in the Port of New York after a cruise in tropical waters.*

HANS MARX

Wind and sun are a welcome combination after the hours of a fire-room watch below.

Those tell a pilot exactly how many more feet the ship is to be moved until she is in line with the dock gangway. It will be lowered in place aboard the ship, and over it the passengers will go ashore.

Now the ship is barely moving. Her sailors have put heaving lines on the dock. Hawsers are snaking down, pulled by the dock workers who make them fast to strong steel bollards. The hawsers are tightened and more are sent ashore, fore and aft. Passengers crane out over the promenade deck below the bridge as the dock gangway is lowered into position.

The job is finished. The quartermaster is told by a watch officer, "Very well, the wheel." A junior officer rings down on the wheelhouse telegraph to the engine room, "Finished with engines."

The tugs start to back away, out into the river. The pilot boards his own boat, and she turns, too, and heads downstream. Another job is coming, and the pilot has only a short time in which he can relax.

5

DURING WORLD WAR II, a New York harbor pilot described
how he went aboard a deeply loaded cargo ship. "They had
her so full," he said, "I had to step down onto her from the
tug."

The pilot did not exaggerate much. Wartime brought
strange conditions to all ships' crews and pilots in every seaport
in the country. New York handled nearly two-thirds of the
troops and the various supplies being sent overseas to the com-
bat areas. It served also as a base for the small craft that were
used to do scout work against enemy submarines in the Atlantic and the boats that kept the harbor safe. Among those were
many former yachts and fishing vessels, and the tugs. They
made a fine record.

The usual peacetime work of a large seaport like New York
is directed by a Coast Guard officer who is known as Captain
of the Port and has his office in the famous United States Cus-
toms Building at the foot of Battery Place, looking right out
over the harbor. The Captain of the Port gives advice about
the movements of naval ships and changes of regulations in
port traffic and safety. The Maritime Association of the port
provides daily listings of the ships that come in and leave. An
organization called The Harbor Carriers of the Port of New
York controls the work of more than 1,200 motor tankers,

barges, lighters, and scows. It is a nonprofit organization, and the men who work aboard the boats belong to four separate unions.

A Western Union ticker tape, mentioned in an earlier chapter where dispatchers' work was described, helps a good deal in the port work. It reports the actual arrival and leaving times of all ships coming into or going out of the port, as they pass Sandy Hook or the government quarantine station at Rosebank, on Staten Island.

When they have some free time, veteran tugboatmen like to tell about a little-known part of World War II history. This is the story of the way tugs moved 10,000 tons of ammunition, gasoline, and rations onto the Normandy beaches in France to support the allied troops after their initial assault. The decision was made at General Eisenhower's headquarters in February, 1944, several months before the attack was made, to bring the necessary equipment from the United States. The British ports had been so badly bombed by the Germans that very few barges or tugs were left.

The job was given to the Chief of Transportation for the United States Army. Then it was turned over to the War Shipping Administration, and tugboatmen were called in to handle it. Rear Admiral Edmond J. Moran, U.S.N.R., who had the rank of captain at the time, was put in charge.

He knew that the craft used must be shallow draft, so they could be placed on the Normandy beaches at high tide. This was very important; the cargo could be taken out only at low tide, and the men who did the work were almost certain to be under German fire. Many different kinds of craft were studied, and finally New York harbor car floats and oil-carrying tank barges were chosen as the best.

But it was hard to get the owners to lend the equipment. There was plenty of work for all available car floats and tank

Her decks empty of troops but with her many life rafts and double-nested lifeboats in place, P 115 is started towards her pier by the neat diesel tug Dalzelleagle.

barges. And, the owners pointed out, this was the early-spring season when the Atlantic gales blew furiously from the west. Car floats were not built to take heavy seas; their hulls would collapse under the pounding.

The problem was solved after tests showed that if one car float was put on top of another, there would be enough hull strength. They would ride piggyback and safely make the Atlantic passage.

So a car float was placed in a floating drydock. It was filled with sea water and sunk in the lowered dock. Then a second float was set on top of the one that was sunk. The water was drained from the lower float. When it was completely pumped out and made watertight, it was raised and the two floats were secured as a single unit.

Work was also done on the oil barges to make them seaworthy. They had been designed for harbor and river use, and needed additional hull strength. The whole expedition, when it was ready for sea, consisted of 12 car floats and 12 barges.

Crews were recruited along the coast, serving under the command of Captain Moran and holding their duties as part of the Merchant Marine. An escort force of Navy vessels guarded the convoy; and twenty-one days after it left New York it entered the English Channel in good shape.

The huge invasion was planned for the first week in June, and time was short. Captain Moran prepared the car floats and barges as soon as possible, their cargo put aboard in a port in southern England. The United States Army had sent over small tugs to handle the craft. These tugs weighed 210 tons apiece, and were brought to Europe on the decks of freight ships.

When officers from General Eisenhower's staff inspected the tug-and-tow flotilla just before the invasion, they admitted that the Germans would be surprised. The car floats still bore on their sides the names of the owners—Pennsylvania, New York Central, New Haven, Baltimore and Ohio. The railroad companies were matched by the names on the sides of the oil barges—Texaco, Socony, and Bushey.

The flotilla was so successful in action that it was more than doubled. There were finally twenty-eight additional car floats and numerous pieces of harbor equipment in service off the Normandy beaches. They, too, had been towed across the Atlantic, then towed from their English base ports to the beaches.

Antiaircraft guns had been mounted aboard the tugs, and they were badly needed. Along with the rest of the immense number of Allied vessels in the stormy waters of the Channel off the beaches, they were savagely attacked by low-flying German planes. Tugs were sunk; men in the crews were killed. Others took over as gunners when their shipmates were wounded, and put up protective fire, drove off the Junker 88's, the Stukas, and Messerschmitts.

The tugboatmen also handled an even more important job under Captain Moran's command during the first anxious, hectic weeks of the invasion. The Germans had never seriously counted on the Allies making an attack in Normandy. Hitler's generals thought the enemy would need regular ports like Cherbourg or Le Havre to put enough men and equipment ashore.

The Germans were wrong. The Allies built two artificial harbors and towed them into place across the channel. Some of the old ships used to make the harbors were hauled from 200 miles away. First, what were called phoenix ships—high, box-like, concrete structures—were towed to the beaches and sunk in place. They were used as breakwaters to protect the landing craft which carried the infantrymen ashore.

The harbors were known as Mulberry American and Mulberry British. Immediately after they were built, a severe gale struck, and the American harbor was almost destroyed. Tugboatmen hauled the material to repair it from England; and the ammunition, the gasoline, the rations, and medical supplies kept on moving steadily ashore.

Tugs hauled thousands of web-steel sections that became miles and miles of highway. Linked together, the sections ran from the pierheads to shore and over the wide stretches of sand on the beaches to firm ground.

The United States used at Normandy big towing craft called V–4's, each of which carried a crew of forty officers and men and a gun crew. The entire tug fleet comprised more than 200 vessels, half of them American. The rest were French and Dutch, and manned by their own crews. The most difficult job was handling the caissons that were placed half a mile offshore.

These caissons were 200 feet long, and when filled they displaced 6,000 tons, almost as much as an average-sized ship. The pierhead sections, set closer inshore, had crew quarters and space for storage. They were big enough to take landing craft alongside to unload troops and vehicles and various kinds of material. The big, bridgelike road sections were brought in on concrete or steel pontoons.

General Eisenhower and the Allied commanders had very high praise for the tugboatmen when the Normandy beaches were secured. But the tugboatmen themselves held great respect for the special task force that had gone ashore weeks before the main attack.

It was made up of men who moved at night in complete darkness among the German electrified mines. Even the slightest contact set off 1,000 pounds of explosives. The men were looking for vital information.

They came back with it. This was used for new charts of the

beach area. Details were given about how the bottom shelved, and where the shallows were. The effect of the tides and the currents was found. Without this information, the whole Normandy invasion might have become a terrible failure.

6

BARGES LIKE THOSE used in the Normandy invasion are kept busy in peacetime. One made the run recently from Frankfort, a Lake Michigan port, to Weehawken, New Jersey. The tugboatmen who hauled her considered it a fairly long tow. The run took her by the inland water routes across half the North American continent.

The barge carried a load of liquid caustic soda. Her name was *Oil Transfer No. 32*, and tug and tow left port on a fine morning in late May. The tug headed north from Frankfort, towards the Straits of Mackinac. Her captain held her close to shore; it was smoother sailing and a shorter course, and he was out of the way of the ship traffic in the middle of the lake.

The loaded barge weighed 2,400 tons, and along this stretch of water the captain preferred to push the craft instead of tow her astern on a hawser. He checked the speed he made with landmarks ashore and with the tugboat's chart. The tow was making 8.7 knots, which meant 10 shore miles an hour. He was content, and figured he would reach the Welland Canal within three days.

The weather stayed fine and clear. The tug captain took a bearing, using his compass when the tow was abreast of Sleeping Bear Point. It was a huge, treeless expanse of sand, but ahead there were bushes and trees on South Manitou Island. The lake was calm and shone bright in the sunset.

During the night, though, the weather changed. Wind picked up and the captain put the barge astern on a hawser that reached 1,200 feet, almost a quarter of a mile. Her lights showed clearly, and were watched with care. The tow was approaching the straits, and would soon pass under Mackinac Bridge, where there was always ship traffic.

It was eight o'clock in the morning before the tug and barge came to the high-rising, beautiful bridge. A deckhand on the foredeck of the tug thought the cars on the bridge roadway looked like ants. But he figured, too, that from the bridge, the tug and the barge looked like water bugs.

When he had cleared the Straits of Mackinac, the tug captain set a course along Lake Huron which would take the tow into Lake St. Clair and then past Detroit. The weather was still rough, and back aboard the barge, her crew were doused by spray when they moved around the deck.

But the next day the lake was calm, and the surface seemed as smooth as salad oil. Tug and tow passed Port Sanilac Light, Huron Lightship, and beneath the Blue Water Bridge. This was the entrance to the St. Clair River, and there was a lot of traffic.

Big, lanky Lakes ships that burned coal for fuel swung out into the lake from the river, moving fast. They left wide black banners of smoke and straight white wakes. The ocean-going ships that were here with cargo for ports on the upper lakes burned oil for fuel. That only sent a brownish haze above their stacks. The ships seemed stubbier and broader than the Lakers, but their bows were sharper and more graceful.

Ships moved in a steady procession past the tow. An Indian from the Canadian side sat fishing in a rowboat, although this was the Detroit River and the Ambassador Bridge was overhead. The skyline of Detroit glittered; it was sunlight on thousands of windows in the office buildings.

The United States mail boat *J.W. Westcott II* came alongside the tug fast, off downtown Detroit. Mail, laundry, and
groceries were put aboard the tug. Two of the tug's crew were
being relieved. They jumped down aboard the launch. The
pair of relief men scrambled onto the tug, and the launch drew
rapidly away into the channel. No line had been used; the
boats had just matched each other's speed.

Down off Bob-Lo Island, below the city, the tugboatmen
were happy to see a tug at work. Her name was the same as
that of the old outlaw, *Jesse James*. On the end of her towline
she had a large ship that had been converted into a barge. A
self-unloading rig had been added, and the barge carried bulk
cargoes of iron ore and coal.

There were stormy-weather conditions again out in Lake
Erie after the tow left the river. The captain headed over close
to the Ohio shore for shelter. He kept along it until he had to
change course for Port Colborne at the entrance to the Welland
Canal.

While the tow waited to get into the canal, it tied up against
a dock wall. The crews from the tug and the barge stretched
their legs, walking the streets of the quiet Ontario town. Then
they watched a Norwegian freighter, the *Norholt* of Oslo, go
into the first of the canal locks, followed by a Dutch freighter,
and a tug and her tow. The men from the two crews were not
impatient.

There was a pleasant parklike space with benches beside the
canal. They sat on the benches or talked with the crews from
the other vessels. Norwegians and Dutchmen were able to
make themselves understood, and a lot of ship gossip was exchanged before they went back aboard.

The tug and tow headed for Weehawken got into the re-
ceiving lock early the next morning. The tugboatmen found

that it had a drop of only a few feet and was 1,380 feet long. But the lock after that had a drop of more than 40 feet, and at Thorold the craft were lowered 140 feet in three steps.

The cook got off the tug in Thorold and went uptown for some shopping. He came back with his arms full of bags of groceries and rejoined the boat at the third lock. Then the tow cleared the breakwater and started out across Lake Ontario. The lake was smooth, but misty, and the deckhands kept a sharp lookout.

It took the tow fourteen hours to cross Lake Ontario and reach Oswego. The tug crew began to get busy for the Barge Canal, where there was very little clearance overhead. The masts were taken down, and the radar antenna, and even the lifeboat davits, and the searchlights were mounted on the roof of the pilothouse. Twin searchlights were set up on the forward ends of the barge, and the tow was ready.

The Oswego Canal led to Three Rivers and the Erie Canal. Enough history was recalled to get the facts straight about the Erie. It had been called "Clinton's Big Ditch" back in the 1820's by the men who thought Governor De Witt Clinton would never finish the job. They had been proved wrong, of course; it had been opened in 1825, and a considerable part of it was still in use.

The tug and tow moved through the locks in the beautiful Mohawk Valley and the long stretches where flowers bloomed in the fields, cattle grazed, and people sat and fished on the canal banks.

Troy was at the eastern end of the canal, and when the tug and tow left the lock there they were in the Hudson River. Albany was passed in the rain, and the next morning they were off Poughkeepsie. Men in the crews who were born New Yorkers were beginning to get homesick.

Newburgh was over there, and these were the Highlands. The broad waters of the Tappan Zee were straight ahead, and rising past them were the bluffs of the Palisades. The Spuyten Duyvil Bridge was next, and when George Washington Bridge was overhead, tug and tow were in the Port of New York.

Oil Transfer No. 32 was tied up at her Weehawken pier in the middle of the afternoon. The haul from Frankfort had taken seven days and four hours. But ten minutes later, on orders from the chief dispatcher for the company that owned the tug, she was given another job.

She was sent over to Todd Shipyards in Brooklyn to pull a freighter from a berth at a pier out into the river. Then she was given work off the Manhattan piers, shifting ships. Before dark, *Oil Transfer No. 32* was unloaded. The tug picked her up in Weehawken and put her towline aboard.

Tug and tow started immediately on their way back to Frankfort, Michigan.

7

TALK WITH A TUGBOAT MAN and he will say that the hardest of all jobs in his trade is an ocean-going tow in storm conditions. He recalls standing by the towing bits, ax in hand, on the after deck of a tug where waves lashed head high. The ax was poised to cut away the towing hawser. Too much sudden strain on it would drag the vessel being towed bow-under beneath a wave. A single extremely severe yank would be enough to send the tow and her crew in a quick plunge to the ocean floor.

The job of guarding the hawser is so tiring in storm conditions that a deckhand can take only an hour of it at a time. He wears what is called "weather gear"; a low-brimmed rubber sou'wester hat, a long raincoat, and rubber seaboots that reach the knees. Still, the seas crest in over the side and douse him from head to foot. He is shivering, numb, just about able to stand and hang onto the ax when his relief man arrives.

Veteran tugboatmen speak with great admiration about the attempt made by the British tug *Turmoil* in 1951 to save the American freighter *Flying Enterprise*. The mate from *Turmoil* got aboard the American ship, which lay dangerously over on her side in a howling Atlantic gale. There were big cracks in her deck and hull plates, and her cargo had shifted. Her master, Captain Kurt H. Carlsen, who was alone on the ship, had sent off the passengers and his crew in lifeboats.

The two men stayed aboard the badly damaged ship for some days while *Turmoil* tried to tow her into a British port. Then, as the gale continued, she listed more and more and finally capsized. When water started to pour down the stack, Captain Carlsen and the tugboat mate, Kenneth Dancy, scrambled aboard *Turmoil.* The tug had moved in dangerously close to get them. The ship capsized and sank, rolling over, immediately after they left her.

There have been many fully successful rescues in the Atlantic, the Pacific, and in the Caribbean. Tugs owned by a number of companies have made them. One large American company keeps tugs in Bermuda, Jamaica, and Panama for ocean rescue and salvage work.

A rescue in conditions just about as severe as those met by *Flying Enterprise* and *Turmoil* was handled safely during the winter of 1964–65, and lasted for nineteen days. Gale-force winds blew all along the Atlantic coast from the Gulf of St. Lawrence as far south as Cape Hatteras. Most of the damage to shipping was done, though, off the Canadian coast. The seas there ran 40 feet high, and spray froze on the ships' wheelhouse windows; the decks were thickly covered with ice.

A Lebanese freighter was beaten so hard in the Gulf of St. Lawrence that she went out of control. She could no longer be steered. Her crew watched helplessly while she piled up, a total wreck, on the Magadalen Islands.

A French ship fought the storm off Burgeo, Newfoundland. She lost and sank. Seven of her crew were drowned and four others froze to death. Eighteen men got away in two lifeboats. They kept rowing and bailing and knocking the thick crusts of ice from the boats' hulls. Their strength lasted, and they survived.

The big British freighter *Prospero* was out in the open ocean, more than 1,200 miles northeast of Boston. She was a converted tanker that carried bulk wheat cargoes between Canada and Great Britain. When the seas hammered her hour after hour, her propeller loosened on the shaft, finally dropped off, and left her powerless.

The 544-foot ship drifted broadside in the storm. That meant she lay deeply in the troughs between waves higher than her masts. She rolled heavily and was taking water aboard. Her master, Captain John Smith, knew she was in very serious danger and might capsize. He decided to send a distress call and ask for help. The radio operator got a message through almost immediately to Boston. The American tug *M. Moran*, stationed in Boston, was ordered on December 19 to make the rescue attempt.

She was an ocean-going vessel that had sailed 22,000 miles to Korea on her maiden voyage in 1961–62. Her master was Captain Alexander De Vane Stewart, and her crew were all veterans. Fuel, supplies, and fresh water were taken aboard at her Boston pier, and she shoved off to try to find *Prospero*.

The tug had 3,500 horsepower diesel engines. She made her best possible speed. But the storm was still blowing. Captain Stewart was not able to come within sight of *Prospero* until five days later. The white-hulled British ship, riding high between the dark seas because she carried no cargo, was seen from the pilothouse of the tug.

Signals were exchanged. Captain Stewart drifted his 300-ton craft downwind towards the lurching, pounding ship. A heaving line was passed, then the steel towing cable was secured. Maybe the British crew would have a fairly happy Christmas now, the cook aboard the tug told his shipmates. But aboard here he was going to lay out the very best he had.

He printed the menu on the blackboard in the tug's galley early on Christmas morning. It read:

Hearts of Celery—Stuffed Olives—Fresh Shrimp
Cocktail
Cream of Tomato Soup
Roast Tom Turkey, Giblet Gravy, Popular Stuffing
Roast Prime Ribs of Beef au jus
French Cauliflower—Buttered Green Peas
Glazed Sweet Potatoes—Whipped Cream Potatoes
Steamed Pudding with Lemon Sauce
Apple Pie à La Mode—Fruit Cake
Hard Candies—Mixed Nuts—Mixed Fresh Fruit
Fresh Milk—Coffee—Tea

The men who came to dinner in the galley found that every item the cook, Anthony Sena, had advertised on the black-board was ready to serve. Most of the crew followed the old shipboard rule and ate fast but heartily, went straight down the menu. It was difficult for them to stay seated at the table and to keep their plates off the floor, harder yet for Anthony Sena as he brought the turkey or the roast beef from the oven.

The wind was blowing fifty miles an hour out of the west. The tug could not make any headway with the tow. She pitched and rolled and banged, and right outside the galley door waves rushed and slammed. The steel door was tightly shut; still a fine spray came through, and outside the portholes wave crests reared up before they hit the side of the deckhouse with tremendous blows.

The men ate their way down to pie à la mode and fruit cake, drank a couple of mugs of coffee, and filled at least one pocket with hard candies and mixed nuts. Then they went back to work. There was nothing out on deck for the deckhands to do, though. A man would lose his life instantly in the seas that crashed aboard. He would either be crushed against the deckhouse or the deck itself, or flung over the side to drown. The deckhands kept a lookout watch up in the pilothouse, and it was down in the engine room that the crew was really busy.

The chief engineer and his assistant walked back and forth between the smoothly humming diesel engines, the pumps, and the generators. Every bit of horsepower was needed now to keep the twin propellers turning. Captain Stewart or his mate, Carl Johnson, stood at the steering wheel and the engine controls in the pilothouse. They held onto the wheel, their feet spread wide, as they looked through the stern windows at the tow.

Prospero was almost out of sight in the great seas, fountains of spray leaping up over her bows as she rolled first on one side and then the other at the end of the towing cable. There was not much to be done with her until the storm let up, Captain Stewart knew. His tug weighed 300 tons. *Prospero* weighed 17,000, and in her light condition, with the wind against her, she was extremely difficult to handle. He would be lucky if he could keep contact with the British ship.

Captain John Smith, the master of the *Prospero*, later told about what had happened to his ship. He said, "We were having very rough weather. Our compass platform on the top of the wheelhouse was carried away by a wave. The weather was constantly bad, with frozen spray. The waves threw us over on our beam ends.

"Our most hectic moment was when the towing cable snapped on Boxing Day.

"Boxing Day—that's the day after Christmas. I suppose it's called that because everybody takes their presents back in boxes to exchange at the stores.

"But when the cable broke it was dark night, with the sea roaring. The weather had got rapidly worse, and was really bad, with great black squalls of wind of hurricane force. The tug was obviously in bad trouble. My heart was in my mouth. How they hung on so long, I don't know. There was nothing I could have done if she had gone over."

When he got to port, Captain Stewart told the tugboat story: "It was five minutes of ten on the night of December 26, and we were laboring in a west-southwest storm, seas thirty feet or more high.

"We were lifting up on the tops of the waves and then slipping backwards.

"Our twin propellers, which had been out of the water a moment before, caught hold in a wave, and we thrust ahead. The cable simply could not take it any more.

"It sounded like a six-inch cannon when it snapped."

The tug had been trying for three days to tow *Prospero*. The job had made the tugboatmen very nervous; they had known right along that in weather like this the cable might snap. Now they felt so relieved they laughed and slapped each other on the back. By herself, the tug could take the worst the storm had to give.

Captain Stewart said, describing the men's feelings, "We chuckled; we laughed; we roared. The tension was gone, if only for a while. Because we would never have abandoned the ship and her crew."

The tug stood by two or three miles away from *Prospero* during the rest of the night. Captain Stewart found at dawn that the British crew were good sailors and brave men. Working in the dark and in storm seas, they had hauled aboard the ship the heavy steel towing cable. That was, they believed, their one chance of being saved. So they brought it aboard *Prospero* and had it ready to give to the tug for another try.

But Captain Stewart took advantage of a momentary lull in

the storm on December 28 and took the tug alongside *Prospero*. The tug put her nylon hawser aboard the ship. She again began to tow, although the weather was very bad.

The wind blew more than 80 miles an hour. Captain Stewart began to worry about his fuel holding out, but the tug bounced around too much to get an accurate measurement of what was in the tanks. Then the storm became worse. It was so bad on December 30 that Captain Stewart had to let go the hawser. He was afraid that the nylon would snap, and then there would be very serious trouble.

"We had an inch of water in our engine room," Captain Stewart said. The tug's chief engineer, Stanley Mikalsen, was afraid sea water would reach the main switchboard and cause a short circuit. Then, the electric power cut off, the tug would drift as helplessly as *Prospero*.

It was January 2 before the storm slacked off enough for Captain Stewart to bring the tug back alongside the battered ship. A heaving line was cast and caught. The nylon hawser was hauled aboard the high bow, and again the tug started to tow.

Captain Stewart opened the throttles wide aboard the tug and pulled with all the power she owned. The tow moved at a little better than two miles an hour for part of a day. Then the storm returned with great fury.

But the tug crew did not take in the nylon hawser. It stayed in place through the fierce, black nights of January 3 and 4 and kept *Prospero* safely astern. The wind slackened on January 5, and Captain Stewart was glad. The treacherous shoals of Sable Island, known among sailors as The Graveyard of the Atlantic, was not far beyond his course to the northward.

"We did not have sixteen hours of straight towing work during the entire job," Captain Stewart said.

He brought tug and tow along the Nova Scotian coast and into the big port of Halifax without any more serious trouble, though. Sea-battered, their paintwork chafed away by the action of the waves, they passed the city, moved through the harbor shipping into the quiet of Bedford Basin. They anchored there, close to each other.

It was eleven o'clock at night on January 7 before the towline was back aboard the tug. The job had taken nineteen days, and Captain Stewart had seen the worst storm conditions of his career. But he still had energy left to go over aboard *Prospero* to meet Captain Smith.

He considered Captain Smith to be a brave man and a very good sailor. It was time they shook hands.

8

WHILE THE CREW of the American tug were in Halifax, they heard the story of a famous Canadian towing job. It had been done during World War II, and the ship saved was the United States Army transport *Wakefield*. She had served before the war as the passenger liner *Manhattan*, sailing out of New York, and was a large and valuable vessel.

The main part of the rescue work was the responsibility of an old coal-burning tug with two high, skinny smokestacks, an iron hull, and mahogany decks. She was 156 feet long, and beside one of the modern American tugs, designed for diesel power and streamlined, she looked almost comical. But out in the wastes of the Atlantic she had proved her worth time and again. Her owners, Foundation Maritime, a Halifax tugboat company, were very proud of her. They had named her *Foundation Franklin*.

She went to the aid of the *Wakefield* on September 4, 1942, after the transport caught fire at sea. *Wakefield* had sailed from New York the day before and carried eight hundred construction workers. These men were bound for Belfast, in Northern Ireland, and were to build a naval and air base. The Germans considered them as important as a contingent of soldiers, because there were several fires in various part of the ship, and all at the same time. No evidence of actual sabotage was ever found, but it was very likely that the fires were started by German secret agents.

Foundation Franklin was 200 miles away to the west when she received the radio message sent by the transport. The fires were out of control aboard *Wakefield*; the ship had been abandoned. The construction workers and the transport's crew were being taken into port aboard the United States Navy vessels of her escort. Four United States Navy tugs were ordered to sea from New York and Boston to get *Wakefield* into port.

The job might have been done without *Foundation Franklin*'s help. But she lay at her dock in Halifax ready to sail. The burning ship was also in the area that the United States Navy had turned over to *Foundation Franklin* for salvage and rescue work.

Captain Harry Brushett told the tugboat's chief engineer to get up steam. She shoved off at full speed and headed on an easterly course for the *Wakefield*. The next morning, at dawn, an American destroyer came slashing through the gray seas at 30 miles an hour and ordered *Foundation Franklin* to follow her. Captain Brushett, forty-three years old and a husky veteran, was amused. The tug was already making her best speed, which was 13 miles an hour.

Then he and the rest of the tug crew saw the *Wakefield*. The 20,000-ton ship was a grim spectacle. She wore gray wartime paint, and already along her hull were big brown blotches from the heat. Smoke hung over her in a thick, dark cloud. The wind, from the west and picking up, would soon blow harder. The heat of the fires was going to get worse.

Captain Brushett knew what he must do. He did not hesitate or slow the tug's speed as he approached the ship. The three United States Navy destroyers that guarded the transport from German submarine attack circled slowly around her at a distance of several hundred yards. They disappeared occasionally into the wind-flattened smoke from the *Wakefield*, but they kept a sharp watch, Captain Brushett knew. The men he was about to put aboard the ship would have a chance to secure the towline.

Wakefield lay motionless in the water, her engines dead. Captain Brushett brought the tug in close alongside her, swung the wheel hard, the spokes spinning. The tug's stern was within 6 feet of the shipside. Big rope cargo nets, which had been used when the *Wakefield's* people abandoned her, still hung from her main-deck rail.

The second mate aboard the *Franklin*, a man named Cecil Bellfountain, and three sailors leaped together. They went from the tug's stern and grabbed the cargo nets and hung on, and then climbed fast. The shipside was so hot the nets were scorched, and aboard the tug the paint on the stern had begun to blister.

Bellfountain waited only long enough on the main deck for a heaving line to be tossed from the tug. Then he and the sailors ran fast, with big, hopping strides to the bow of the transport. They passed the heaving line around a sturdy steel bitt and sent the free end down aboard the tug.

The powerful windlass aboard the tug reeled in the heaving line, which served as a messenger. The line, as it was hauled in by the windlass, sent up to the men on the bow of the ship the tug's heavy steel towing wire. Bellfountain and the sailors with him shackled the towing wire in place, then thought about getting back aboard the tug.

They had been aboard *Wakefield* for about twenty minutes. It took them no more than that to secure the heavy wire. Their feet had started to blister, though, inside their thick-soled shoes. Their hands were seared by contact with the almost red-hot steel, and their eyes were bleary with smoke. They were

partly blinded when they made the leap down aboard
Franklin.

Captain Brushett had steered the tug within feet of the
ship's bow. He held her with her broad stern deck towards
Wakefield. The men could jump down onto the rope hawsers
coiled there. But the tug was pitching sharply with the motion
of the seas. He knew that he would be lucky if all his men got
back aboard without being hurt.

But they made it all right, landing safely on the hawsers.
Captain Brushett sent the tug at full speed ahead. He wanted
to get *Wakefield* moving. The towing cable drew out taut
astern, and *Franklin* thrashed the sea with every bit of her
power. Officers aboard the United States Navy destroyers
watched the work through binoculars, and Brushett could
imagine their expressions. They were laughing at him.

The old two-stacker, with all her huff and puff and the big
white wake kicked up by her propeller, got nowhere. She
weighed 600 tons; *Wakefield* weighed more than thirty times
that much. It was an impossible job.

Still, the smoke cloud over the transport had begun to
change shape and direction. The transport moved. The smoke
from her was trailing astern. *Franklin* trembled fore and aft
with the effort. She hauled the transport towards Halifax at a
little better than two miles an hour.

Captain Brushett stood relaxed in the pilothouse while the
mate relieved him at the wheel. Any time now, he realized,
the four United States Navy tugs that had been called by
radio would be here to take over the tow. The destroyers could
take care of German submarines, but with all their power they
could not help with the tow job. They were not equipped for it,
and would only injure themselves if they tried.

The tugs appeared a few hours later. *Franklin* was allowed

to keep her towing wire aboard the ship, but Brushett was told that the United States Navy was in command. He was also told by the commander of a big diesel tug who bawled at him through a megaphone, "Keep that hay-burning barge out of my way! We've got a job to do!"

Captain Brushett did not answer. He was very interested in the way the Navy tugs started their part of the tow. Three of them put their wire cables aboard *Wakefield*. The fourth secured hers on *Franklin*'s bow. Then the wind rose and became storm.

The tugs could not steer against the rough, high seas and still keep their wires aboard *Wakefield*. One of the United States Navy tugs snapped her cable with a loud report. Captain Brushett, who had not forgotten his craft had been called a hay-burning barge, got rid of the towline secured on *Franklin*'s bow. He ordered a deckhand to take an ax and chop through it. The deckhand was pleased to obey. The other two Navy tugs had just slipped their cables, afraid that if they kept them secured to the tow, they would capsize.

Franklin kept on alone for Halifax with *Wakefield* in tow. The Navy tugs gathered together downwind. They kept discreetly out of the way, their captains aware that they were not built for this kind of rough-weather work in the open ocean.

Captain Brushett brought the still-burning transport through the minefield into Halifax harbor. He beached her at McNab's Island, and the American naval vessels assembled in the port greeted him with repeated whistle blasts. Canadian and American fire tugs pumped water into *Wakefield* for a week afterwards and at last put out the fire.

It was decided by American naval authorities that the ship's hull could still be used. *Wakefield* was going to be converted to an aircraft carrier at Boston Navy Yard. The tow job was given to a United States Navy tug and to *Franklin*, with Captain Brushett in command. The Navy tug towed on the port bow, *Franklin* on the starboard. *Wakefield* was safely delivered in Boston.

Captain Brushett returned to Halifax on October 5 aboard *Franklin*. He was completely exhausted, and three days later he was in the hospital. The doctors said that he suffered from what was very nearly paralysis of the legs; he should stay in the hospital for months.

He reported for work a month afterwards and insisted he was fit to take *Franklin* to sea. The company needed him. There were all kinds of jobs to be done. First, he hauled a collier off a rocky shore in the middle of a snow gale. Then he went looking for some tugs that had gone adrift in the same storm. He was happy, even though his legs had started to hurt him again and it was hard for him to stand and look out the pilothouse windows.

9

STORMS THAT PICK UP force across thousands of miles of empty ocean cause a great deal of damage to vessels of any size. But the narrow channels in sheltered, supposedly modern harbors are dangerous, too. Most tugboat work is done in harbors, and every year the ships that are handled get bigger. The tugs have less turn-around and backing space. Their crews must be very careful, and sometimes a pilot aboard a ship being towed makes a mistake. The result is disaster.

It was a clear and lovely day on June 16, 1966, when two ships and their tugs approached each other in New York harbor. They were between Staten Island and New Jersey, moving through a narrow stretch of water known as the Kill van Kull. One ship, an 11,000-ton British motor tanker, named *Alva Cape*, was loaded. She carried in her tanks 132,000 barrels of naphtha, which she had taken aboard in Karachi, India. The other ship, the 16,500-ton American tanker *Texaco Massachusetts*, was light, having just pumped out her fuel cargo at a dock in Bayonne.

Visibility was very good. The crews of the two ships could see each other while they were several miles apart. Passengers in automobiles crossing over the Bayonne Bridge could look down upon the officers and the pilots as the ships moved closer. There did not seem to be any danger. This was a routine job for both ships. Then there was confusion; whistle blasts were too late, and neither ship could change her course in time.

Alva Cape was on a westerly course, headed along the Kill van Kull into Bayway, New Jersey, to pump out her very flammable naphtha cargo. The tugs *Esso Massachusetts* and *Esso Vermont* were with her to help her to her dock. An experienced harbor pilot was on her bridge beside the ship's captain.

Texaco Massachusetts was coming south along the channel, the tug *Latin American* alongside her. She, too, had an experienced harbor pilot aboard who knew every foot of the channel, which close ahead formed a right-angled, dog-leg turn. *Alva Cape* was about to swing around and make the dog-leg turn. Both vessels kept on moving, while their whistles brayed a series of signals that did not make sense.

They met bow-on and with great force. The Number One tank aboard *Alva Cape* was split open, and hundreds of tons of naphtha leaked down her side and covered the water. The two ships and the three tugs, now almost motionless, sat in a lake of the stuff.

The collision occurred at two twelve in the afternoon. There was no fire or explosion for three and a half minutes. The masters of both ships hoped they could get away from the naphtha spill and take their vessels to safety. But the tug *Latin American* kept her place close alongside *Alva Cape*. She was drenched by the naphtha as it slopped down over her from the smashed tank.

Latin American burst suddenly into flame fore and aft. Naphtha fumes had seeped into her engine room. She was a small vessel, 97.2 feet long and only 165 tons. The naphtha turned her into a terrible torch.

Flame leaped in a huge orange spurt, and *Alva Cape* was afire. The flame was so intense it seemed to take away all daylight. There were one hundred and ten men aboard the five vessels, and staring, they saw fire come at them from the surface of the water. The naphtha lake was burning, and there were explosions aboard *Alva Cape* that rocked her from her bow to her stern.

Pinnacles of flame and smoke erupted over the span of the Bayonne Bridge. The alarm was given immediately to the Coast Guard, the New York City Fire Department and the Marine Division of the Police Department. All harbor craft were warned by shortwave radio to stay out of the Kill van Kull.

The alarm was received in the dispatcher's office at the Moran Company, but a tug had already been sent. The diesel tug *Julia C. Moran* happened to be at a dock in Port Richmond, Staten Island. Her captain was George Sahlberg, and he was told by radio telephone at two fifteen to "get over to Bergen Point. There has been some trouble."

Captain Sahlberg had shoved off at once and made the short run to the Kill van Kull at top speed. As he neared the scene he saw that both ships had dropped anchor, and that they had suffered collision damage. But there was still no fire. Captain Sahlberg kept going ahead towards the tankers. His tug was about 400 yards away when *Alva Cape* exploded.

He saw men on the British tanker whose clothing caught on fire as they crossed the open deck and jumped overboard. The water into which they plunged was aflame. They would have very little chance to live unless he risked his tug and her crew.

Captain Sahlberg kept the tug moving into the flame. He had called all of his men on deck, and hand-lines were ready over each side of the tug to bring survivors aboard. The *Alva Cape*'s men looked up and waved their arms and called, "Save us, please!"

Julia C. Moran saved twenty-three men. *Esso Massachusetts* moved in close, and her crew pulled out fourteen. Both tugs were caught within sheets of flame, but were able to back away without serious damage being done. Other tugs had begun rescue work; fireboats and Coast Guard cutters and picketboats and Police Department launches joined them. The fire aboard *Alva Cape* was fought with high pressure hoses and a chemical-foam compound that smothered the stubborn flames.

Captain Sahlberg took his load of survivors into Port Richmond, where ambulances waited, then went back again to the Kill van Kull. The wind was brisk out of the southwest. The huge tank farm at Bayonne, whose reservoirs held millions of gallons of gasoline, was only a short distance away across the channel. If *Texaco Massachusetts* caught fire and exploded— and it seemed likely that she would—half of the New Jersey port area around there would become charred ruins.

Texaco Massachusetts was almost as dangerous as the British tanker because she was empty and did not carry cargo. Her tanks had not been cleaned and highly explosive gases were in them. Those could be set off by a single spark, and then she would blow up like an enormous grenade.

Veteran tanker men stood on the docks in Bayonne and watched with amazement when a tug went alongside *Texaco Massachusetts.* They knew how great a chance the men from the tug were taking. The ship had been abandoned. Her people were gone, and her captain had died of a heart attack while he tried to swim from her.

But two tugboatmen were determined to save her, at least get her out of the Kill van Kull. They came from a tug named *Helen L. Tracy.* Their names were Thomas Gibney and Arthur Biagi, and they worked aboard the tug as mate and as deckhand. Gibney was a Navy veteran who had also served in the Fire Department fire boats. Biagi was much younger and had less experience, but he was strong and quick moving.

They went up onto the tanker's main deck over a boarding ladder raised from the tug. The tanker's deck plates were still hot, and the deck was knee-deep in fire-fighting foam. Their job was to raise the anchor so the ship might be towed. Tugs that tried to haul her now would tangle her anchor flukes in the Staten Island–Bayonne telephone lines that reached across the bottom of the channel.

Gibney and Biagi were able to raise the anchor. They locked in the anchor windlass by hand and lifted the big, 7-ton hook clear of the bottom. But that was slow work. While they were at it, other men boarded the tanker and got her ready to be moved.

Inge Norberg, the mate from a second tug worked alone on the top deck of the tanker. Hand over hand, he dragged up very heavy hawsers and secured them. Those came from his tug and from a third. The crew of *Helen L. Tracy* had already secured a wire cable to the ship's anchor. So, all told, three tugs would join in the tow attempt.

Ole Ericksen, who was captain of one of the tugs, had gone up into the tanker's wheelhouse. He tested the wheel and got a response from the steering mechanism. There was still some power left. He did not know how long the power or the ship would last.

The paintwork in the wheelhouse was blistered. The windows through which Ericksen stared held glass cracked by the heat. Naphtha fumes stung his eyes and nostrils. Smoke from the *Alva Cape* laid a thick, black, greasy blanket across this ship, and he realized that the British tanker's bunker fuel had also caught fire. It would be a long jump down from here if there was an explosion.

But, squinting through the smoke, he was able to see *Helen L. Tracy*. The wire cable that led from her towing bitts to this ship's anchor was taut. Captain Ericksen peered out over the

On a fair day with full visibility the 604-foot American tanker S.S. Texaco Massachusetts (left) was in collision with the 546-foot British tanker M.V. Alva Cape. This happened on June 16, 1966, in New York harbor in a section known as the Kill van Kull Channel. The channel is between Staten Island, N.Y., and Bayonne, N.J. Tugs are hauling the Texaco Massachusetts out of danger; although she carries no cargo she still contains very explosive gas fumes. A New York City fireboat and a Coast Guard cutter try to put out the blazing naphtha cargo aboard Alva Cape. Notice the big gasoline tanks in the foreground, which, with the wind, can catch fire any moment.

Flame ripples down the gashed hullside of Alva Cape while she rests, deserted, almost under the Bayonne Bridge. Her crew and the crew of the Texaco Massachusetts abandoned ship as the fire aboard the British tanker became worse. The captain of Texaco Massachusetts died of a heart attack while swimming in the fire-covered water near his ship.

side. The other two tugs had taken a strain on their hawsers. The ship was beginning to move.

Captain Ericksen steered for twelve minutes, and greatly helped the work of the tugs. Then there was no more power left from the ship's boilers. The last of her steam pressure was gone, and the steering engine would not respond to the wheel.

It was time for him to go. He got quickly out of that gloomy, lonely place and boarded his own tug. That vessel and the other two tugs hauled *Texaco Massachusetts* from the Kill van Kull. They took her to a safe anchorage off Brooklyn.

Meanwhile, *Alva Cape* smouldered and flared. For days she was too hot and dangerous to approach. At last a salvage crew was put aboard her on June 28 to attempt to pump out the rest of her cargo. A large part of the naphtha, kept in separate tanks, had not caught fire. The men pumped in air and brought the naphtha out through hoses and put it aboard barges. They worked with great care.

But *Alva Cape* exploded again, and four of the salvage crew were killed. The Coast Guard declared the flame-scarred wreck a menace to navigation in the port. She had cost the lives of thirty-seven men.

A pair of tugs was assigned to tow her to sea. The deckhands who boarded her with the towing hawsers wore soft-soled shoes and worked very fast. She was hauled from her anchorage in Gravesend Bay and into the open ocean off Cape May, New Jersey. Two Coast Guard cutters went along as escort.

The cutter *Spencer* was given the job of sinking her. The Coast Guard gunners fired fifty-seven rounds of 5-inch ammunition before the tanker broke in the middle and sank. She disappeared beneath a towering column of her own smoke and flame. The depth there was 1,200 fathoms, and the position was more than 150 miles southeast of Manhattan. That was a

U.S. COAST GUARD

A Coast Guard helicopter closed with the Alva Cape *although the ship might spray exploding naphtha hundreds of feet in the air. New York City fireboats and Coast Guard tugs pour water and chemicals into her. Over beyond her, the tugs stubbornly pull* Texaco Massachusetts *clear of the British ship. Thirty-three men have just lost their lives in the collision here.*

MORAN TOWING & TRANSPORTATION CO., INC.
JEFF BLINN, PHOTOGRAPHER

Alva Cape *was towed from the Kill van Kull to a broad channel in lower New York Bay. But on July 2, fireboats still kept putting water aboard her. She had burst into flame again at this anchorage and killed three men who worked to save her and what was left of her cargo. Now tugs of the Moran Company get ready to tow her to sea. The Coast Guard has decided she is too dangerous to remain afloat. She is marked for destruction, and Davey Jones will get her.*

MORAN TOWING & TRANSPORTATION CO., INC.
JEFF BLINN, PHOTOGRAPHER

The Coast Guard cutter Spenser *destroys* Alva Cape *with a series of shell blasts off the Continental Shelf in the deep Atlantic.*

good resting place for her; she had caused one of the worst ship disasters in New York harbor history.

Captain Sahlberg, for his handling of *Julia C. Moran* and the rescue of twenty-three of the British tanker's crew, was given a very special award. It was the medal for heroism, presented by the American Bureau of Shipping. When the medal was pinned on Captain Sahlberg's lapel at a ceremony in December, 1966, he was told that this was only the fourth time in thirty-seven years that it had been presented.

The president of the Bureau of Shipping said, "It was meant to be a rare award to be made only in recognition of extreme cases of valor, and Captain Sahlberg is eminently qualified."

Captain Sahlberg blinked in the glare of the television lights mounted around the bureau office and directed on him. He said, grinning, "It's brighter here than when the *Alva Cape* blew up."

The entire crew of *Julia C. Moran* received in November, 1967, the Gallant Ship unit citation of the United States Maritime Administration. This was for their heroic conduct in the *Alva Cape* rescue work. The bronze plaque that recorded the event was fixed on the tugboat's deckhouse alongside the midships door.

Several awards were made at the same time to the other tug captains who had participated in the rescue work. The men were glad that the ceremony was held in the open air and on Pier One, close alongside *Julia C. Moran*. There were no television lights, and a quick jump would put them aboard.

10

VETERAN TUGBOATMEN still talk with affection about the coal burners whose hulls were made of pine planking and whose bows carried great, beardlike hemp fenders. But they are happy aboard the modern boats. They have become accustomed to the powerful, steel-hulled diesel craft, are ready for change, and welcome any improvements in engines or design.

Great Lakes crews are extremely interested in a new type of tug recently put in service in the Port of Chicago. She is the diesel-powered *Arizona*, owned by the Great Lakes Towing Company. Her regular pilothouse is down on deck in the usual position. But she has another pilothouse, located on the end of a boom that can rise 50 feet straight up in the air.

This extra pilothouse is mounted on extensible hydraulic rams. It can swivel in any direction or move horizontally so the pilot can peer around any obstruction. The pilot's vision is never blocked. He can see around his tow and also over the cargo aboard the barges that *Arizona* pushes.

Arizona does a great deal of work in narrow channels and rivers. The pilothouse perched aloft on the end of the boom has already saved a considerable amount of damage to the tug herself and her barges. When she comes to one of the many bridges she must pass under along the winding waterways where she works, boom and pilothouse are lowered down on

A novel and extremely useful type of tugboat pilothouse is mounted on a hydraulically operated telescopic arm that lets Great Lakes captains get an unbroken view of what's going on around them.

deck. They fit snugly out of the way beside the stationary pilothouse. The pilot just shifts from one to the other and keeps the tow moving.

West Coast tugboatmen are very interested in a new craft that is only 22 feet long. She is the motor tug *Teakerne Spinner*. Her width is half her length, so she looks like an old-fashioned bathtub gone adrift.

But she is actually an extremely efficient little work horse. *Teakerne Spinner* has a number of unusual features in her design. She does not need a rudder or reverse gears. Her 200-horsepower diesel engine sends its power to a propeller that can be swung on a vertical 360-degree axis. This means the tug is able to turn around within her own length.

She was built in Vancouver, British Columbia, for use in the logging industry. Her owners are Macmillan Bloedel, Ltd., and she is the first boat of her special type. She has a reinforced hull and good all-around visibility, and her design allows her to operate when she is surrounded by logs.

Teakerne Spinner works most of the time in Puget Sound. Her jobs are handling logs dumped from barges, and moving big, made-up booms that are really thousands of logs chained together. She spins ahead, or spins astern, and in any direction her captain wants to take her. The strongly built hull shoves loose logs away without damaging her, and her propeller is safe, out of danger beneath her. She might resemble a bathtub, her admirers admit, but she gets plenty of work done.

Tugboatmen on both coasts are keenly curious about the craft used on the Mississippi River. Some of them are even a bit jealous of the Mississippi River pilots, whose reputation for skillful boat-handling is known around the world. They have heard or read about the boats used in the inland trade and which are made on the very latest designs.

The *Kathryn Eckstein* is one of these. She was built in St.

Designed specially for work in West Coast logging operations, this craft can turn around in her own length. Her kind is badly needed in the Puget Sound area where masses of huge logs are moved.

Louis for Wisconsin Barge Line. Her twin diesel engines give her 5,000 horsepower. They are controlled from the pilothouse, and she can move twice the load handled by any other boat of her kind built earlier. She can also keep the same speed as her competitors through the toughest part of the river.

This is between Cairo, Illinois, and New Orleans. Her load weighs 45,000 tons. *Kathryn Eckstein* handles 30 barges, which are strung out before her, solidly lashed together with wire cable and chains. Each loaded barge weighs 1,500 tons, and the tow takes up acres of space in the river. But Captain Aubrey E. Turner navigates it without too much trouble. He is a good example of the river pilots who were first made famous by Mark Twain.

There are in active service today only a few hundred fully qualified pilots. A man has to put in at least three years of duty aboard the towboats before he is allowed to sit for his examination by the Coast Guard and receive his license. He must know every beacon and day-time marker and buoy along the section of the river for which he is licensed, and these he memorizes. Along with these, he gets to know the locations of various landmarks, islands, shoals, and sandbars. He can tell the river depths and the effects of the currents.

The pilotage is almost the same as the work done by Great Lakes or seaport tugmen. But there is a great deal of difference in handling the tows. It was learned years ago on the Mississippi that a string of barges hauled astern could not be kept in line. They swung widely, yawing right or left with a cross current or wind, ended up adrift, wrecked on rocks and against concrete or steel bridge piers.

Rivermen were not quick to make the change, and push the tow instead of hauling it. They waited fifty years, and even then they kept the name and called their craft towboats. But the boats cannot tow anything larger than a skiff. They are

Powerful diesel-equipped Kathryn Eckstein *handles an immense "tow" all by herself, Mississippi River style. She pushes instead of hauls her barges, which are held together by a complex system of chain and wire-cable lashings. She is on her way from Cairo, Illinois, to New Orleans. Her thirty barges weigh 1,500 tons apiece and take up acres of space.*

square-bowed, and the bows hold the massive pair of steel towing knees which reach nearly as high as the deckhouse.

A modern Mississippi boat is equipped with three propellers, ten rudders, two searchlights, a radar, a fathometer for checking river depths, a gyroscopic compass, an automatic steering control, and a radio telephone. There are also in the pilothouse a mobile telephone, which can be used to call a number anywhere in the world, a telephone to talk to the engine room, a telephone to talk to the members of the crew who are working out on the barges that make up the tow, an announcing system, and a radio receiver for regular programs. The console located by the forward windows of the pilothouse holds the controls for steering the boat and adjusting speed, and all the gauges needed to operate the engines.

The barges stretch for almost half a mile in front of a modern Mississippi River steamboat when she is at work with a tow. It takes the captain and the mate hours of study with thin pieces of wood about the size of dominoes to get a tow organized. Each piece of wood represents a barge. One is loaded with steel pipe; another is empty; a third carries cement; a fourth is filled with grain. They are checked against a list and a mimeographed plan from the company's port captain that tells where the various barges are supposed to go.

When a down-river voyage starts from St. Paul, up near the headwaters of the Mississippi, a towboat captain knows that he has at least one thousand hours of pilotage to do before he reaches New Orleans. The worst part of the river work is below Cairo, because of the force of the current and the large amount of traffic. The river there is winding, too, and constantly changing. New banks and bends and cutoffs appear on each trip to confuse a pilot.

Headed downstream at night with a loaded tow, a pilot needs all of his training. He knows that the tow will not stop

The two-stack diesel Freeport Sulphur *shoves a smoking-hot liquid load of sulphur up the Mississippi from New Orleans. Notice the fumes rising from the barge vents.*

going around a bend. The best he can do is steer the towboat out into the channel at the next bend. Most of his barges are already there, and if he meets an upbound tow, there will be a serious collision.

But the river helps. He "flanks"—half slides—around the bend and gets safely into the stretch of straight water below. When he meets the next upbound towboat, he sounds a greeting blast on his air horn, and is given a blast in answer. New Orleans does not seem so far away.

INDEX

The Author

ROBERT CARSE is a well-known author of books for young people and adults. His recent historical works for young readers include *The Young Colonials, The Great Lakes Story, Great American Harbors, The High Country, The Young Mariners,* and *Ocean Challenge*. He has also written books for adults about the famous clipper ships and the early days of the American merchant navy.

An experienced seaman, Mr. Carse has spent the same amount of time on the water as on land during the last forty years. He has sailed as an able seaman, gunner, master-at-arms, deck watch, and chief mate. During World War II he served aboard merchant ships in every theater of operations for four years. Mr. Carse's wartime experiences form a background for *The Long Haul,* a nonfiction account for young people of the United States Merchant Marine in those dangerous years of war at sea.

Mr. Carse and his wife live on Shelter Island, just off East Hampton, Long Island.